THERE'S
AN
ELEPHANT
IN YOUR
OFFICE

THERE'S AN ELEPHANT IN YOUR OFFICE

PRACTICAL TIPS TO SUCCESSFULLY IDENTIFY AND SUPPORT
MENTAL AND EMOTIONAL HEALTH IN THE WORKPLACE

ASHLEY SIDES JOHNSON
ANDREA SIDES HERRON

Published & distributed by:
Ashley Sides Johnson and Andrea Sides Herron

in association with:
IBJ Custom Publishing
One Monument Circle, Suite 300
Indianapolis, IN 46204
www.ibjcustompublishing.com

ISBN 978-1-939550-95-8
First Edition

Library of Congress Control Number: 2019938237

Printed in the United States of America

IBJ CUSTOM PUBLISHING

CONTENTS THERE'S AN ELEPHANT IN YOUR OFFICE

INTRODUCTION

You may not realize it, but there's an elephant in your office.

Most everyone sees the elephant and knows it appears in the break room around 11:30 and sits in the 3rd cubicle on the left. However, no one really mentions it. No one acknowledges the presence of an elephant in a business setting unless there's a deafening roar or stampede, and even then, no one talks openly about what just happened. They just exchange quizzical looks and whisper to each other behind closed doors.

Is there an elephant in your office? There are nearly 44 million of them in the United States, so the odds are good that one of them shows up to your workplace every day.

Is the elephant a single parent? Veteran? Person age 55 or older?

Nope. The elephant in your office is a person experiencing mental illness.

According to the National Alliance on Mental Illness (NAMI), approximately 1 in 5 adults in the U.S.—43.8 million, or 18.5%— experiences mental illness in a given year and approximately 1 in 25 adults in the U.S.—9.8 million, or 4.0%—experiences a serious mental illness in a given year that substantially interferes with or limits one or more major life activities. So, why do managers, leaders, and colleagues keep ignoring them? Why do they pretend to not see the elephant standing right in front of them until a coworker or major project gets trampled?

- Fear
- Uncertainty

- Self-preservation
- Ignorance
- Denial

We think the reasons for not dealing with mental and emotional health in the workplace are a bit different for everyone, but the outcomes are the same. Elephants—people experiencing an episode of poor mental health—subconsciously know that the office environment is not safe for them. If someone figures out their secret, these elephants fear they could lose their jobs, be demoted, or humiliated. The elephants feel scared, insecure, unable to talk about their needs, and generally try to remain invisible.

How can a culture of secrecy and denial where stigma prevents employees from reaching their full potential possibly make a company or business stronger? It can't.

In this book, we—Andrea (HR professional) and Ashley (communication specialist with a diagnosed mental health disorder)—will use our collective knowledge and experiences to help people on all rungs of the corporate ladder notice, identify, and properly interact with—even supervise—employees experiencing a mental illness. By starting this conversation, we hope to enlighten business people and give elephants across the country a better chance at success.

1 in 5 adults in the U.S. experiences mental illness in a given year.

1 in 25 adults in the U.S. experiences a serious mental illness in a given year.

All employee examples are real and stem from our work across the country spanning decades. We've changed names and any other identifying information to protect everyone involved.

1
ELEPHANTS

If you walked into a new office, spent 10 minutes meeting the employees and were then asked to identify which employee currently experiences a mental illness, could you do it?

If the assignment involved identifying which employee wore a neck brace or sat in a motorized wheelchair, there would be no issue. Those physical attributes are easily recognized. But how do you decide which person experiences a mental illness when it's virtually impossible to see from the outside? You might as well try to figure out who has diabetes, heart disease, or irritable bowel syndrome.

The ability to blend in with the herd and not be singled out is a particular specialty of elephants in the workplace. But, before we talk about recognizing elephants in the office, it's important to have a basic understanding of the species as a whole.

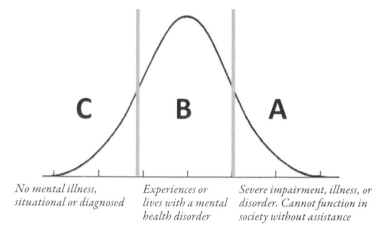

No mental illness, situational or diagnosed

Experiences or lives with a mental health disorder

Severe impairment, illness, or disorder. Cannot function in society without assistance

This image is a standard bell curve. It's used in research, business, science, and lots of other industries to illustrate the distribution of people, resources, or other measurement along a continuum. We're using it to show where various members of our elephant species appear along a continuum of mental well-being.

In the graph above, a person in perfect mental health would be placed on the far left of Section C. People who experience situational depression or anxiety and those with a diagnosed mental illness but considered high-functioning fall in the middle, Section B. Those on the far, right side of the curve—Section A—have a severe mental illness or developmental disorder that substantially limits life activities.

If you work with and/or manage people, it is important to understand the basic differences between the three sections.

SERIOUS/SEVERE MENTAL ILLNESS (SECTION A)

The National Alliance on Mental Illness (NAMI) says, "Serious mental illness (SMI) is defined as a mental, behavioral, or emotional disorder resulting in serious functional impairment, which substantially interferes with or limits one or more major life activities."[1]

The organization goes on to say that "Mental disorders typically meeting criteria for serious mental illness include schizophrenia, schizoaffective disorder, psychotic disorders, major depressive disorders, bipolar disorders, and borderline personality disorder. Anxiety disorders (such as obsessive-compulsive disorder and panic disorder) or eating disorders (such as anorexia nervosa and bulimia nervosa) can also meet criteria for serious mental illness."[2]

DEVELOPMENTAL DISORDERS (SECTION A)

The term "developmental disorder" or "developmental disability" means a severe, chronic disability of an individual that:

- is attributable to a mental or physical impairment, or combination of mental and physical impairment
- is manifested before the individual attains the age of 22
- is likely to continue indefinitely
- results in substantial functional limitations in three or more of the following areas of major life activity:

  - self-care
  - receptive and expressive language
  - learning
  - mobility
  - self-direction
  - capacity for independent living
  - economic self-sufficiency
  - reflects the individual's need for a combination and sequence of special, interdisciplinary, or generic services, individualized support or other forms of assistance that are of lifelong or of extended duration and are individually planned and coordinated.

As defined by the Developmental Disabilities Assistance and Bill of Rights Act of 2000, Public Law 106-402.[3]

Because the criteria for Section A in our bell curve includes "severe impairment, illness, or disorder" and "cannot function in society without assistance", people with a developmental disorder would most likely be placed in that section. While we aren't focusing on employees with developmental disabilities in this book, it's helpful to understand where they fit on our continuum.

MENTAL HEALTH DISORDERS COMMONLY FOUND IN THE WORKPLACE (SECTION B)

The following conditions account for the majority of employed people who experience a mental health disorder in a given year.[4]

It should be noted that common disorders such as anxiety and depression can be persistent or episodic. A person diagnosed with major depressive disorder as a teenager will most likely have to manage that illness throughout their life. (They are most likely to be in Section B of the bell curve.) Conversely, a person experiencing the death of a family member or friend may have a period of depression. With some counseling and time, they recover from the episode. (They most likely move from Section B to Section C of the bell curve.)

Anxiety Disorders

Anxiety disorders are a group of related conditions, each having unique symptoms. However, all anxiety disorders have one thing in common: persistent, excessive fear or worry in situations that are not threatening.

Bipolar Disorder

Bipolar disorder causes dramatic highs and lows in a person's mood, energy, and ability to think clearly.

Depression

Depression is more than just feeling sad. It's a change in behavior that lasts more than two weeks. Common symptoms include significantly more or less sleep and appetite, lack of interest in activities, loss of energy, feelings of hopelessness, and thoughts of suicide.

Eating Disorders

Eating disorders are a group of related conditions that cause serious emotional and physical problems. Each condition involves extreme food and weight issues but has unique symptoms that separate it from the others.

Obsessive-Compulsive Disorder

Obsessive-compulsive disorder causes repetitive, unwanted, intrusive thoughts (obsessions) and irrational, excessive urges to do certain actions (compulsions).

Posttraumatic Stress Disorder (PTSD)

PTSD is the result of traumatic events, such as military combat, assault, an accident, or a natural disaster.

NO IDENTIFIED OR DIAGNOSED MENTAL ILLNESS (SECTION C)

Most of the workforce occupies space in Section C. These employees can cope with the normal stresses of life, work productively, relate to others, and make choices. As such, they are said to be in good mental health. Over the course of a lifetime, we expect these people to ebb and flow within the boundaries of Section C. Some may even experience a major life change and take up residence in Section B for a short time.

RECOGNIZING ELEPHANTS

For the purposes of this book, when we talk about elephants, we're talking about people in the middle and left sections of the bell curve—Section B and Section C. These people are considered functional by behavioral health providers. They can successfully hold a job, complete their assigned tasks, etc. or else you wouldn't have hired them. We are not talking about people in the right section of the graph (Section A) who have developmental disorders like Autism, ADHD, Cerebral Palsy, etc. or people with severe mental illness. People diagnosed with these conditions can absolutely contribute to the success of their community, but they don't represent a large portion of the workforce so we will save that topic for another time.

Now that we have defined the scope of our book and provided an overview of the entire elephant species, it's time to dive into specifics. **To help you recognize elephants in your current office or those in potential workplaces, we've divided the herd into three groups:**
- **Amazing Mammoths**
- **Invisible Elephants**
- **Rampaging Pachyderms**

Each pack looks, behaves, and communicates differently. Understanding these attributes is essential to properly identifying and supervising the elephants in your office.

2
AMAZING MAMMOTHS

Have you ever been to the circus? If so, chances are good that you saw a giant elephant balance on top of a tiny ball. That ball is now your employee. Under normal circumstances, the ball can move and shift with ease. It might roll or bounce or be tossed up into the air. It's a consistent size and shape and behaves like a ball every day. But isn't this book about elephants? Yes. The elephant in this metaphor is an external stressor for your employee.

That could include situations such as:

- Ending of a relationship or marriage
- Losing or changing a job
- Death of a loved one
- Developing a serious illness (yourself or a loved one)
- Being a victim of a crime
- Having an accident
- Undergoing a major life change (such as getting married, having a baby, or retiring from a job)
- Living through a disaster, such as a fire, flood, or hurricane

Behavioral health professionals call a short-term condition that occurs when a person has great difficulty coping with, or adjusting to, a particular source of stress, such as a major life change, loss, or event an **"adjustment disorder."** (In 2013, the mental health diagnostic system technically changed the name of "adjustment disorder" to "stress response syndrome" but most people still use the original phrase.)[5]

Because people with an adjustment disorder/stress response syndrome often have some of the symptoms of clinical depression, adjustment disorder is sometimes informally called "situational depression." While this description makes sense, an adjustment disorder doesn't involve as many of the physical and emotional symptoms of clinical depression or high levels of severity such as suicidal thinking or behavior.

A person with an adjustment disorder/stress response syndrome develops emotional and/or behavioral symptoms as a reaction to a stressful event—not brain activity or genetics. Noticeable behavior may include problems with a person's ability to function, e.g. studying, completing tasks, and focusing. The key indicator of an adjustment disorder is greater or more intense reaction to the stressor than what is typical or expected for the situation or event.[6]

We don't have a statistic for this statement, but believe that almost everyone has experienced a life event that resulted in adjustment disorder. Any time you have complete upheaval to your schedule, family, or health, it takes a while to adjust to a new normal. This is part of processing emotions and generally being a person.

In the past, most employees could set aside their personal issues during the work day because there was a distinct separation between work and home. The two did not intermingle. As kids, if we needed to talk to mom or dad during the day, we had to call the business telephone number and ask whomever answered the phone to get mom/dad so we could talk to them. We were taught to only do this for REALLY important stuff because it interrupted their job performance and tied up a business phone line.

With the advancement of technology, we've actually made coping more difficult by eroding the barrier between work and home. In the digital age, communication never stops. Countless apps, programs, and devices keep us tuned in to every minor, major, and imagined crisis. Employees can't focus solely on work when their phone or watch keeps dinging with messages from mom, dad, grandma, the babysitter, teacher, or the kids! And that's just a normal day. The interruptions are ten-fold when a loved one experiences a health event, prolonged illness, arrest, incarceration, or addiction. In these situations, the employee can't focus on work because there is a constant reminder of what's happening at home.

For people with an adjustment disorder, these life events manifest as a two-ton, floppy-eared elephant determined to smash anything underfoot. And no matter how much they want to be successful in their assigned tasks, the weight of the elephant on top of them makes it nearly impossible.

How do you identify Amazing Mammoths?

Employees experiencing a major life event look the same as they did yesterday or last week. They don't appear on a Monday morning in a wheelchair, wearing a back brace, or an eye patch because a relationship ended or a loved one received an unexpected diagnosis. If internal struggle manifested as visible, physical impairments, Amazing Mammoths would be super easy to identify! Instead, these elephants experience subtle changes in appearance and behavior as the weight of their external stressor increases.

Because they are preoccupied with their situation, struggling with grief, or distracted by new tasks, personal appearance may take a back seat. That could look like more days with long hair in a messy bun or ponytail; more make-up to cover under-eye bags or less make-up because it takes too much effort; ties and socks that used to match perfectly no longer coordinate; uniforms look wrinkled and worn.

In addition to the new disheveled look, Amazing Mammoths may change how they interact with others. Morning discussions about sports and weather while making coffee in the breakroom turn into a quick head nod and "good morning." Office doors are closed more often and social interaction as a whole, decreases. Managers and coworkers might notice this shift in behavior before they realize an employee's grooming and accessorizing skills have diminished.

Another possible indicator of an Amazing Mammoth is presenteeism.

Presenteeism is defined by the National Center for Biotechnology Information as "the problem of workers being on the job, but, because of illness or other medical conditions, not fully functioning."[7] Companies figured out years ago that employees who are physically absent from work can negatively impact the financial bottom line. Following an article titled, *Presenteeism: At Work—But Out of It* appeared in the Harvard Business Review in 2004, companies began to measure productivity losses due to employees who are physically present but not working at capacity.[8]

Causes of Presenteeism[9]

1. **Dual-earner household** – Dual-earner families account for 48% of all married couples, according to the Bureau of Labor Statistics.[10] Without a stay-at-home spouse to care for a sick child, many workers will go to work when they, themselves, are ill in order to save their limited sick days for when their children are sick.

2. **"Sandwich generation" households** – 25 million American workers provide informal care for an elderly family member or friend who needs help with basic personal needs and daily activities. They do this while raising their own children so they are "sandwiched" between the generations.

3. **Employer expectations** – In today's often "leaner-and-meaner" workplaces, some workers trudge off to work when sick because they fear one or more of the following: appearing less committed to their jobs, receiving disciplinary action, or even losing their jobs. A day or more off can also mean burdening coworkers with job duties, coming back to a heavy backlog of work responsibilities, or missing work deadlines.

4. **Little or no paid sick days** – A 2017 report from the Bureau of Labor Statistics shows that on the average, 68 percent of private industry workers have access to paid sick leave. But the highest percentage of workers who receive paid sick leave fall into

management and finance occupations. The average percent of workers in service and construction jobs that get paid sick leave is respectively 46 and 47 percent. As a result, many workers are reporting to work when ill to avoid loss of pay. *Sick leave laws vary by state.

The causes of presenteeism cited above by business professionals could double as a list of external stressors waiting to trigger adjustment disorder in an employee. Remember, it's not the actual situation that constitutes an adjustment disorder. It's the subsequent—and short-term—reaction that occurs when a person has great difficulty coping with, or adjusting to, a particular source of stress.

Here are a few examples to help you recognize Amazing Mammoths in the workplace.

True Story: Maria

Maria, a bubbly, outgoing sales professional had been on the job for about one year when her father passed away. Her usually sunny and engaged demeanor shifted drastically after she returned from bereavement leave. Although she still hit her deadlines, Maria's direct reports noticed that she wasn't as present or interested in their meetings and initiatives. She kept her door closed more often than not and didn't engage in friendly chit-chat anymore. Simply put, she was in a deep state of mourning.

After seeing this first hand and overhearing comments from her team, the HR partner decided to check in on Maria. Maria had previously told the HR partner that her father passed away, so the HR partner asked her how she was handling the recent loss. Immediately, Maria started crying. She told the HR partner that she thought she was hiding it well but acknowledged that she felt emotionally raw and hadn't been on her game lately at work. The HR partner let her know that she was human and allowed to have human feelings. She also reminded Maria that she had resources available through the EAP (Employee Assistance Program), support groups in the area, and close colleagues who cared about her to help get through it. At the end of the conversation, Maria thanked the HR partner for checking in and said she would use some of the resources available to her.

Although it took a few months, Maria's support group helped her return to her bubbly and outgoing self. Did she still have an occasional *off* day where grief unexpectedly showed up? Of course, but now she had the tools to address her feelings without negatively affecting her department or employees.

True Story: Zach

As a new manager in the company, Zach walked into a tense departmental situation where a long-time manager was replaced with an employee from a different area of the business. His task included bringing two separate employee factions into the same department under a new manager and changing the direction of that department's work. Anger, hostility, and frustration consumed the employees.

After some team building and HR intervention, things in the department began to normalize. That improvement was short-lived as Zach became distant, easily provoked, and dismissive at work. On at least three business trips, he got ridiculously drunk and combative and humiliated the staff members travelling with him. Seeing the boss's behavior as permission to regress, employees retreated into their former factions. Hostility and unprofessional behavior returned. Over a period of a few weeks, Zach managed to dismantle the team he worked so hard to construct.

Several dark months passed and employee morale was in the dirt when Zach started appearing in the office more frequently. He spoke with employees and engaged in the work of the department. His entire demeanor changed and everyone was confused. Thanks to some top-notch social media sleuthing, a staff member figured out that Zach experienced marital problems and now lived alone.

Had Zach told the department manager he was experiencing some personal issues, the manager could have tactfully and appropriately talked with staff members. Alternatively, had Zach mentioned something to a trusted person in the HR department, those HR employees assigned to work with his department could have provided better guidance to his staff when they came to HR out of frustration.

True Story: Ruby

Ruby was a consummate professional with a good track record. One day, she was attending a major final proposal meeting for a challenging client. At the end of the call, thinking the phone was on mute, Ruby said "I hate this client" under her breath. Unfortunately, the call wasn't on mute and the client heard the comment. This was very uncharacteristic behavior for Ruby and obviously a big deal for the company.

The managers decided to send Ruby home for the day so they could discuss what to do. In the meantime, Ruby had a pre-scheduled meeting with the HR director. The HR director briefly chatted with the manager to make sure everyone was on the same page before speaking with Ruby. When Ruby came in to talk, she was very sullen as she had just spoken about her unprofessional behavior with her manager. She started the conversation by saying, "I was originally coming in to talk to you about maternity leave because I'm pregnant. However, now I'm not sure I need it because I'm probably going to be fired."

The HR person was thrown off by the new disclosure but reassured Ruby that she should feel free to use the resources available to her to begin the process of applying for maternity leave. She also reiterated that based on company policy, a termination was not the only possible outcome for this situation; however, the manager and HR did need to regroup and discuss. Ruby left the meeting very down and frustrated by her actions that led to the situation.

While the pregnancy disclosure provided insight into the unexpected behavior, it did not define the employment decision. Ultimately, Ruby received a written final warning for her inappropriate remarks but was not terminated from her role.

How do you manage/supervise an Amazing Mammoth?

When dealing with Amazing Mammoths, knowledge is power. As a manager or supervisor, you cannot provide resources or help your employee if you don't know something is wrong. Our suggestions:

- Be aware of the normal routine and vibe of your office.
- Pay attention when that vibe shifts or changes.
- Engage in routine conversation with your staff. Seeing them and listening to them provides an opportunity to notice changes in behavior and/or appearance.

If an employee displays signs and symptoms of an adjustment disorder, intervene sooner than later. Don't wait until things get worse.

Try using questions like these:

- I've noticed you have your door closed a lot lately. Is something in our environment bothering you? Someone talks on the phone too loudly? It's too hot/cold when the door is open?
- I sense that you are really stressed. What do you need to find your balance again?
- I want you to be successful but it seems like you're struggling to complete tasks lately. How can I help you get back on track?
- And after reading this book—is there an elephant smashing you?

During your discussion, if an employee relays to you a situation or experience that places them solidly in Amazing Mammoth territory, **use your knowledge and resources to help.** Creating and reinforcing a culture of silence and presenteeism will negatively impact your employees' health as well as the company's bottom line. We think employees struggling to adjust to major life events should be encouraged to use their provided benefits, paid time off, and sick days. Being distracted while on the clock is more costly than an employee taking a short leave of absence to handle their current situation.

DON'T FORGET!
Chapter 2 Summary

- **Adjustment disorder – Short-term difficulty coping with a specific major life change**
- **How do you identify Amazing Mammoths?**
  - Subtle changes in appearance and behavior as the weight of their external stressor increases
  - Presenteeism
- **How do you manage/supervise an Amazing Mammoth?**
  - Be aware of the normal routine and vibe of your office.
  - Pay attention when that vibe shifts or changes.
  - Engage in routine conversation with your staff. Seeing them and listening to them provides an opportunity to notice changes in behavior and/or appearance.

3
INVISIBLE ELEPHANTS

Invisible Elephants are employees with a mental illness who are high-functioning enough to hold a job. For whatever reason (biology, disease, childhood trauma, etc.) the neurotransmitters in their brains have communication issues. This leads to garbled or misunderstood messages that, in turn, cause symptoms of mental illness.

These elephants may take psychiatric medication and see a mental health professional for ongoing treatment or they might try to manage the disorder on their own. Some of these elephants may realize they experience the world in a different way but do not have an official diagnosis to explain it.

At work and in life, Invisible Elephants occupy a more precarious position than Amazing Mammoths or Rampaging Pachyderms. They are the Goldilocks of employees experiencing poor mental health—

too sick to pretend "this will pass" but not sick enough to draw attention to themselves with concerning behavior. They try to act "just right" and hope no one notices the occasional empty porridge bowl or broken chair left behind.

According to NAMI, the following conditions account for the **majority of employed people** who experience a mental health disorder in a given year.

- Anxiety Disorders
- Bipolar Disorder
- Depression
- Eating Disorders
- Obsessive-Compulsive Disorder
- Posttraumatic Stress Disorder (PTSD)

These conditions are identified by mental health professionals using a reference manual called the *Diagnostic and Statistical Manual of Mental Disorders* (DSM). The American Psychiatric Association (APA) creates and updates the DSM based on extensive research conducted by hundreds of international experts.[11] The publication provides trusted information to help clinicians identify, define, and diagnose patients with a psychological disorder. The DSM is also recognized as an important reference for the judicial system, health insurance companies, and government agencies like the Department of Labor and the Equal Employment Opportunity Commission (EEOC).

Here is the complete list of chapters in DSM-5; they represent the most current list of recognized mental health disorders.

The complete listing of DSM-5 chapters:

Neurodevelopmental Disorders	Trauma- and Stressor-Related Disorders	Gender Dysphoria
Schizophrenia Spectrum and Other Psychotic Disorders	Dissociative Disorders	Disruptive, Impulse Control and Conduct Disorders
Bipolar and Related Disorders	Somatic Symptom Disorders	Substance Use and Addictive Disorders
Depressive Disorders	Feeding and Eating Disorders	Neurocognitive Disorders
Anxiety Disorders	Elimination Disorders	Personality Disorders
Obsessive-Compulsive and Related Disorders	Sleep-Wake Disorders	Paraphilic Disorders
	Sexual Dysfunctions	Other Disorders

How do you identify Invisible Elephants?

Regardless of their physical or mental health on any given day, people with mild or well-controlled mental health disorders generally look like everyone else. You could sit next to a person at work every day for years and not know they have a diagnosed mental illness because they are masters of blending into the environment—cubicle camouflage, if you will.

Animals use camouflage all the time as a means for survival. Their goal is to hide in plain sight and not activate their defense mechanisms or engage in combat. Being completely overlooked by a predator guarantees them a win every time.

The same goes for our Invisible Elephants. To them, the office environment can feel just as dangerous as a jungle. For self-preservation, they hide in plain sight instead of using their natural defense mechanisms to confront or defeat a predator. Experience shows that if all goes according to plan, the perceived threat will completely overlook them and move along without incident.

But, if Invisible Elephants are so good at hiding, how are you supposed to find them? And should you even be looking for them?

As the manager, you apply skills and knowledge as it becomes relevant. It's not your job to be nosy and up in people's personal business. Your job consists of identifying potential hazards in the workplace as they relate to business, financial, or human success. We do not advise you to go hunting for elephants, but want you to be familiar enough with the characteristics of the species to properly identify an Invisible Elephant should you encounter one in the office.

The following are warning signs according to NAMI that could indicate the onset, re-emergence, or worsening of a mental illness. If these behaviors appear in your employee, consider activating your plan. (You'll learn how to do that in Chapter 5.)

Warning signs according to NAMI[12]

Each illness has its own symptoms, but common signs of mental illness in adults and adolescents can include the following:

✓ Inability to carry out daily activities or handle daily problems and stress
✓ Excessive worrying or fear
✓ Feeling excessively sad or low
✓ Confused thinking or problems concentrating and learning
✓ Multiple physical ailments without obvious causes (such as headaches, stomach aches, vague and ongoing "aches and pains")
✓ Extreme mood changes, including uncontrollable "highs" or feelings of euphoria
✓ Prolonged or strong feelings of irritability or anger
✓ Avoiding friends and social activities
✓ Difficulties understanding or relating to other people
✓ Changes in sleeping habits or feeling tired and low energy
✓ Changes in eating habits such as increased hunger or lack of appetite
✓ An intense fear of weight gain or concern with appearance
✓ Inability to perceive changes in one's own feelings, behavior or personality
✓ Difficulty perceiving reality (delusions or hallucinations, in which a person experiences and senses things that don't exist in objective reality)
✓ Abuse of substances like alcohol or drugs
✓ Thinking about suicide

Employees exhibiting one or more of these warning signs should catch your attention and prompt further—more detailed and consistent—observation.

To help you connect the dots between warning signs and possible solutions, here are a few examples of what it looked like when Invisible Elephants revealed themselves in the office.

True Story: Juan

Juan serves the community as a first responder. He also has a digestive disorder and recurrent bouts of Posttraumatic Stress Disorder (PTSD). The chronic illness and PTSD can manifest as extreme irritability or depression. That looks like screaming at coworkers, being obviously annoyed that someone needs help, or withdrawing from the crew to be alone. Regardless of how he feels, his mood, or physical symptoms, Juan has to do his job. People's lives literally depend on him.

To help fire, police, and Emergency Medical Services (EMS) employees like Juan cope with the emotional hazards of the job, industry best practice encourages them to create a peer support network. No one from the outside understands the complex emotion generated from a major car accident where an entire family died or the residual effects of saving people from a burning house or hostage situation. But work brothers and sisters get it.

Juan's station uses the peer support network and it has helped him manage episodes of PTSD. The network provides him a safe space to say what's really bothering him without worrying that his fellow officers or commanders will think he's weak or incompetent. This process creates a win-win for Juan, the first responders, and the community.

True Story: Imani

Imani works remotely for an insurance company. As she reached her sixth month of pregnancy, Imani started to discuss maternity leave plans with her manager. Not long after these conversations, her husband called the manager to let him know Imani had suffered a miscarriage and was in the hospital. Imani returned to work two weeks later, insisting that she wanted the distraction. During her first week back, the manager and Imani had a check in to get caught up on the current workload. After their check in, the manager came to HR and let his HR partner know that Imani was back at work but still didn't seem to be herself. He didn't want to pry or dig for information but also wanted to mention it because Imani was having a notably hard time keeping track of the work details and seemed very down.

In their next check-in meeting, Imani disclosed to her manager that in addition to the miscarriage, she experienced amniotic fluid embolism. This condition, where amniotic fluid enters the mother's bloodstream, is very rare with a high mortality rate. Thankfully, Imani was one of the lucky ones who survived but complications from the event left her with short-term memory loss and mental health issues such as depression and anxiety.

The medical complications did not keep Imani from meeting her employment goals, but they changed her overall disposition and ability to focus. As months went on, she continued to struggle with tasks and sounded flat instead of sunny and upbeat as in the past. The manager asked HR what he could do to help and what services the company could provide. Human Resources explained that Imani's situation was a bit more difficult because she worked remotely. No colleagues could observe her mood or behavior and accessing office-based services would be very inconvenient.

Despite these challenges, HR and the manager worked with Imani to find solutions that allowed her to be successful. Together, they identified useful resources in the Employee Assistance Program (EAP), scheduled frequent check ins, created a system to track project details, and the manager remained vigilant in paying attention to any sudden changes in attitude or performance.

True Story: Memphis

A bright and charismatic employee working in the marketing department of a health system, Memphis interacted with community groups, doctors, and employees across all departments. She liked to be involved in projects and tasks and was considered a high-performer. About five years into the job, Memphis' ability to juggle multiple projects diminished. A huge assignment that clearly belonged in her job duties was ignored, and a coworker had to jump in and handle it. Following a series of other failed or neglected tasks, Memphis received a disciplinary notice. This punishment sent her over the edge and she quit her job.

A day or two following her resignation announcement, the department director asked Memphis to come by and talk. The director told Memphis there was a big difference in her work performance now as compared to a couple of years ago. "What happened?" the director asked.

Memphis shared that 18 months prior, the health system changed what prescription medications were covered through the employer insurance policy. Due to this change in the formulary, a medication Memphis took to manage her diagnosed mental illness was no longer available. She had spent the past year going on and off a variety of psychiatric medications trying to find one that worked. The process left her in an extremely fragile state and it took everything she had just to physically get to the office each day. She really needed to take time off or use FMLA, but the work load kept growing and she didn't see a way to put her needs before the organization's needs.

Had Memphis felt comfortable discussing her struggles with a manager, director, or HR person, an earlier intervention might have led to a different outcome. In the end, with some guidance from HR, Memphis arranged to stay on at the health system in a part-time role. This helped the organization maintain institutional knowledge while simultaneously creating a work schedule that supported her success and recovery.

True Story: Dr. Singh

Dr. Singh completed a medical residency and landed his first job as a physician. He did not disclose a history of major depressive disorder and thought he was prepared to handle the demands of treating patients. As it turned out, he underestimated the emotional burden of listening to and addressing people's problems. Day after day of telling patients they had serious health conditions or learning the patient isn't compliant with taking their medication because they can't afford it eroded his resilience.

It didn't take long for the familiar feeling of despair to reappear. Dr. Singh tried his best to push through but others were beginning to notice a change in his behavior. After some discussion with medical leadership, Dr. Singh agreed to take a leave of absence so he could address his mental health condition. Thanks to the support of leadership and his fellow physicians, Dr. Singh successfully treated his episode of depression and put support systems in place to help him in the future.

Under no circumstance should performance challenges or constructive feedback be new information during an annual or mid-year review. It is a best practice to bring up concerns in real time so the employee has a chance to work on it and is not blindsided during review time. It might feel easier to postpone uncomfortable conversations like this, but the conversation actually gets harder the longer you wait.

—Andrea Sides Herron

How do you manage/supervise Invisible Elephants?

Methodically. Sneaking up behind an elephant who is trying to be invisible will startle them and send them stampeding into the jungle. Instead, approach them calmly, but with purpose. Use the power of **regular schedules, consistent work assignments,** and **routine meetings** to help your elephants perform to the best of their ability.

As the boss of an Invisible Elephant, consider creating a structured environment. **Use organizational tools** like calendars and checklists to help your employees know what is expected of them and when. Clear deadlines can remove uncertainty about how a project will evolve or conclude. Meeting face-to-face on a regular basis provides an opportunity to ask questions and review progress but also allows for important conversations to happen organically.

When you're an Invisible Elephant, so much energy is spent trying to blend in that there's rarely enough emotional capital left to handle an unexpected event. That's why sticking to a routine helps. Routines generate a feeling of consistency and security. Knowing what comes next allows these employees to redirect energy normally used for managing symptoms to focusing on assigned tasks. That's a win for them and the business.

Bottom line—Invisible Elephants don't like surprises. As their manager, try to be as transparent as possible about work assignments and expectations. Clear and concise information quiets thoughts of "what if" and worse case scenarios and allows your employee to concentrate on the task at hand—not on whether their cover is blown.

"Come in and close the door"

ASHLEY SIDES JOHNSON

As an Invisible Elephant myself, words cannot adequately describe the emotions generated from being called unexpectedly into your boss's office and told to close the door. I liken it to being held hostage during a bank robbery or walking through the woods alone at night with no flashlight. Without any prompting, your brain kicks into survival mode. Endorphins pump through your body, your heart rate increases, your breathing shallows, and every muscle in your body tenses up in anticipation of a fight to the death.

It doesn't matter that this is an office, and the person before you is a human being. Your brain shut down all logical thought processes as your hand turned the knob to close the door.

What happens next? The (totally normal, everyone has them) voices in your head engage in a screaming match. "Run! Hide! Fight!" says the primal side. "No. Stop it. We're fine," says the rational side. "Danger! Get out now!" says the primal side. "Seriously, it's okay. Take a breath," says the rational side.

With so much noise in your head how can you possibly hear anything the boss is saying? You can't. I mean, your ears process the sound of their voice and you cognitively understand they are speaking, but you can't retain that information. So, one of two things happens next:

- If you are doing what you should to manage your disorder and it's a period of good or well-controlled mental health, you can quell the clamor in your head just enough to nod in agreement with your boss. You sign something if they tell you to sign it, and mumble words of comprehension like, "I understand." You walk out of the office somewhat composed but having no idea what just happened or if you agreed to do a project or task. It's like having temporary amnesia.

- If it's a period of poor mental health and you are barely holding on to sanity, about four words into this conversation you burst into tears, storm out of the office in a fit of anger, or have a physical reaction that leads to vomiting, passing out, or collapsing.

Both scenarios are humiliating for your elephant, and both result in the complete failure of communicating an important message to the employee.

In my opinion, the best way to successfully communicate and avoid unnecessary fight-or-flight responses from your employee involves not calling impromptu meetings and instead, using your regularly scheduled meetings to bring up any concerns.

Consider creating an agenda that you follow each time that contains routine progress reports but also space to discuss opportunities for improvement.

Send a brief email in advance of the meeting if a new topic will be introduced.

If you need the employee to explain a decision or respond to criticism, give them time to process the information. Ask for a verbal or written reply by the end of the next work day or before your next scheduled meeting.

If you really do need to have a confidential discussion about work, try these sentences (I use them with coworkers and it seems to be effective in reducing anxiety.):

- Can you come to my office? I want to ask you about the project deadline. You are not in trouble.
- I need your help with some confidential business. This isn't about you.

DON'T FORGET!
Chapter 3 Summary

- **Conditions that account for the majority of employed people who experience a mental health disorder in a given year:** anxiety disorders, bipolar disorder, depression, eating disorders, obsessive-compulsive disorder, and posttraumatic stress disorder (PTSD).
- **How do you identify Invisible Elephants?**
  - Watch for warning signs that could indicate the onset, re-emergence, or worsening of a mental illness.
- **How do you manage/supervise Invisible Elephants?**
  - Use the power of regular schedules, consistent work assignments, and routine meetings to help your elephants perform to the best of their ability.

4
RAMPAGING PACHYDERMS

Pachyderm \ ˈpa-ki-ˌdərm \ is another word used to describe elephants. While you may see these animals in a zoo or on a nature show and think they are sweet and peaceful, don't be fooled. They can be dangerous and aggressive when provoked by real or imagined threats. As a matter of fact, elephants are known to experience unexpected bouts of rage that lead to rampages and kill hundreds of people each year.[13]

As it relates to the purpose of this book, Rampaging Pachyderms are employees with a psychiatric disorder (diagnosed or undiagnosed) who experience a significantly disruptive episode of poor behavior at work. The episode occurs due to a real or imagined threat and involves the employee displaying an unexpected bout of extreme emotion. Regardless of the underlying cause—fear, anger, confusion, etc.—the Rampaging Pachyderm demolishes anyone or anything in its path. If left unchecked, their behavior threatens the lives of people and the infrastructure of companies.

How do you identify Rampaging Pachyderms?

You can spot a Rampaging Pachyderm from a mile away. Their behavior feels like it's straight out of a movie and you almost can't believe you're seeing what you're seeing. Sometimes the episode starts and ends in minutes leaving a giant patch of scorched earth behind, while other episodes drag on for weeks in a more passive aggressive fashion. Each scenario is unique because each employee experiences loss of control in a separate and distinct way.

The following stories will help you have a better grasp on what a Rampaging Pachyderm might look like in the office and how other professionals intervened in some complex situations.

True Story: Chip

Chip was an average, introverted system programmer that presented as quiet and generally kept to himself. HR started getting reports of him intimidating female colleagues in meetings with an aggressive and demeaning tone and hostile body language. One afternoon soon after these reports were filed, Chip got angry and had an outburst in the office. This was an open work environment and he yelled and threw his keyboard so loudly that people on the complete other end of the building heard the commotion.

HR started an official investigation following this outburst and included the original complaints of intimidation. Through the investigation and interviews with various staff members, it was discovered that Chip had a very aggressive temper and made his colleagues (male and female) feel intimidated and threatened if they were to go against his ideas or suggestions. When the investigation concluded, Chip was given a final warning and put on a performance plan to work toward improving his behavior and relationship with his teammates. He was also given the Employee Assistance Program (EAP) information with a recommendation to reach out for counseling and/or anger management treatment.

For the first few weeks of the performance plan, things seemed to be going better. There were no more outbursts and everyone on the team was trying to give him another chance. However, one day things turned south. There was a particularly heated meeting where Chip stood over a colleague and yelled at them about how wrong they were on the topic at hand. He was visibly angry and red in the face. The manager was called in to calm the tension but the team was shaken up. It was determined shortly after this meeting to terminate Chip's employment immediately.

The manager and HR partner called Chip into a meeting room to discuss the incident and let him know he would be leaving that day. Chip instantly got defensive and blamed his reaction on stress from a pending divorce. When the HR person told him that she was sorry to hear that, but it didn't change the outcome of the decision to

SURVIVAL GUIDE FOR ENCOUNTERING A RAMPAGING PACHYDERM IN THE OFFICE

Should you come face-to-face with a Rampaging Pachyderm:

- Take note of your surroundings—Who is present? Clients? Customers? Other employees? Are there any physical safety hazards in the immediate environment?

- Determine if the "charge" is real or an empty threat. Always err on the side of caution, but as a manager, you may recognize the difference between normal bad behavior for a specific employee and an escalation of that behavior.

- Call for back up. (If the situation warrants, call 9-1-1 for police assistance.)

- Follow your plan for intervention.

- Document, document, document. Once the situation resolves and it's safe to do so, write down everything that happened.

terminate employment, Chip stood up, yelled obscenities at her, and slammed his fist down on the table. She waited for him to take a breath and then calmly and quietly asked him to sit down so they could review some important final paperwork. Because the HR manager diffused the situation and did not meet him at the same level of emotion, Chip was able to regain some level of composure without another major outburst.

Pro Tip:

Speak softly. It's critical in highly tense situations to maintain a calm and quiet demeanor. An irate employee will struggle to remain loud and belligerent if no one is fueling their anger.

Once the paperwork had been reviewed and the meeting was over, HR escorted Chip back to his desk to gather his belongings. He threw his items into his bag as hard as he could and slammed his chair into his desk on the way out. Thankfully, he was not heard from again after that day, although the HR person and manager did look over their shoulder twice when leaving the building that night.

True Story: Tobias

Tobias was recently promoted to a senior level position and was becoming quite the team leader. One weekend, he set off on a camping trip and when he returned home, he emailed his boss that he could not come to work on Monday. He disclosed that during the trip, he uncovered buried childhood trauma and was in the middle of a mental health crisis. Tobias had pre-scheduled vacation time that coming week so the manager said not to worry and that the team would cover while he took some time to work through it. Tobias used a full week of vacation days but informed his manager that it wasn't enough. He then used a week's worth of sick time.

On Thursday of the second week off, Tobias sent a very unhinged, rambling email about his personal and mental health situation to his entire work team. This was troubling to the team for two reasons; it was highly out-of-character for Tobias and they have a right to not know this level of detailed personal information about their coworker. After reviewing this email, the manager stepped in and told Tobias that they needed to talk about his long-term plan since his excused time-off options were nearly depleted.

The manager alerted HR about the situation so they could create a plan on how to best support Tobias and also the business. Tobias, the manager, and a human resources representative scheduled a time to meet offsite on Friday (the day after sending the overly-personal email). During this meeting, the HR representative laid out the various options the company offers to support individuals in tough times. Options included FMLA, short-term disability, and the Employee Assistance Program (EAP), which offers free and anonymous counseling sessions to staff members. Tobias said he was already seeing a counselor but would explore the leave options as he wasn't sure when he would feel ready to come back to work.

The approved time off came to a close and the manager arranged for a second offsite meeting with Tobias and the HR representative to make a return-to-work plan. At the meeting, Tobias exhibited very concerning behavior. He was erratic in his speech and movement, scattered in thought, and struggled to follow any kind of logical discussion. He talked about taking trips and vacations, then announced grandiose plans of going back to school to get a doctoral degree and go into a completely new field of study. He then reported being harassed online, that his car was being controlled by Silicon Valley Tech CEOs, and that he went "undercover" to the auto repair shop so they could fix his car without knowing who he really was.

The manager and HR representative realized that Tobias could not return to work. Because he was out of sick time and vacation time, the HR representative recommended moving him to a personal leave. Following this path would allow Tobias to remain covered through his insurance plan and provide time to file for Family Medical Leave Act (FMLA). Tobias said he understood the suggestion and would complete the paperwork for FMLA. Given his peculiar behavior at the meeting, the manager and HR representative were concerned he would not follow through on the plan.

An official follow-up email with FMLA forms attached and specific instructions given on how to complete and submit the information was sent to Tobias.

A week went by with no response. On Friday, one week and one day after the second offsite meeting, HR learned Tobias was missing and no one had heard from him for almost 24 hours. The entire weekend passed with no news about Tobias or his whereabouts. Finally, late Monday afternoon, HR was informed that he had been found and was currently hospitalized.

Some employees truly need behavioral health services, but it's not advised for an employer to mandate such services. Requiring an employee to take action regarding personal health concerns, like using the EAP to get a therapist, carries a lot of risk. Even riskier is the danger of inadvertently disclosing an employee's medical condition to their manager or other staff member, whether it be real or simply perceived, as that can create a huge liability from both an ADA and HIPAA perspective.

–Andrea Sides Herron

Over the next two weeks, Tobias remained in the hospital but worked with the company to complete and submit FMLA paperwork. His family member (with appropriate permissions granted) provided assistance to the HR representative so Tobias' hospital stay and medications would be covered per the company's medical benefits plan. By the end of his stay, Tobias reported stabilization with his medication and his health care provider gave a return-to-work date.

Four months after the original episode (the camping weekend), Tobias returned to work with no restrictions. The manager and HR representative met with him prior to the first day back to set expectations regarding the need to give coworkers and himself time to re-integrate and be patient as he tried to get up-to-speed.

There were ups and downs the first month for both Tobias and his teammates. Due to his new medication regimen, Tobias appeared more subdued and not quite his former, talkative, enthusiastic self. This was definitely a change for his coworkers to process. Tobias continues to perform at the basic expectation level for his job and appears to be emotionally stable. The hope is with an adjustment period and some time, he will return to the high-performance level experienced before his health episode.

True Story: Brittany

Brittany worked for a non-profit organization in a large city. The office environment was casual with job tasks that involved interaction with clients and coworkers.

Brittany often made inappropriate comments regarding other people's appearance, mannerisms, etc. loudly, in common areas of the office, and with no regard for who may hear her. This created a lot of tension in the workplace as the subject, timing, and recipient of her remarks seemed random. Coworkers tried to keep their distance and people generally didn't like hanging out with her because she brought a lot of unnecessary drama.

After a couple of failed conversations with her manager regarding this behavior, Brittany was written up and put on a performance improvement plan. During subsequent discussions with Human Resources, she voluntarily disclosed past trauma including being raped, having an abortion, and attempting suicide. Brittany said she saw a therapist regularly and took medication. She also claimed that she had multiple personality disorder and border-line Tourette's Syndrome. Brittany made no attempt to provide HR with confirmation of these diagnoses or complete paperwork for reasonable accommodations or a leave of absence. (To be clear, no "reasonable accommodation" would allow derogatory speech or behavior in the workplace.)

Brittany did not succeed in completing her improvement plan. After another outburst and inappropriate comment to a colleague, the organization terminated her employment. In the termination meeting, the HR representative and another manager documented that Brittany was very emotional and volatile. She screamed at the HR representative saying, "You are ruining my life" and "You are making me homeless. Without my job I can't pay rent." She added, "Maybe I should just kill myself."

At that point, the HR representative offered continuation of full, free access to the company's Employee Assistance Program. The program included many services, including behavioral health treatment. Brittany was encouraged to seek out a therapist. The manager and HR representative told Brittany that she was a good person who was in a moment of transition.

Contrary to previous behavior, Brittany left the building that day without screaming or name-calling. As a matter of fact, she looked sullen and sad as she slowly and methodically gathered her belongings. This show of emotion felt staged and attention-seeking even though it was quiet.

Later that week, Brittany posted a profane tirade on social media. In it she stated the company did not care about her and the HR person—listed by name in the post—wanted her to be homeless and without a job. Several employees still working at the company responded to Brittany's post. They encouraged her to look forward to new opportunities instead of being angry. A few employees also notified HR of the post.

Within a few weeks, Brittany found a new job in a different industry and things at the office were quiet for about three months. Then, on a regular Wednesday morning, word came in that Brittany took her own life.

Management and employees at the organization expressed their regret through a lot of "if only" and "we should have" conversations. HR reassured them that their feelings were valid and reiterated that the company could not have legally done anything more for Brittany without infringing on her rights.

How do you manage/supervise Rampaging Pachyderms?

The short answer is, learn to spot the elephants in your office before they turn into Rampaging Pachyderms. Once a person becomes outwardly disruptive with an established pattern of unacceptable behavior, it's really too late for a successful **Human Resources** intervention.

An employee exhibiting concerning mental health symptoms needs to be warmly and appropriately referred to treatment experts, not summarily fired and sent packing.

More importantly, if you believe an employee represents a danger to themselves or others based on their behavior, get them to a safe location, stay with them (if appropriate), and notify Human Resources immediately. If they pose an imminent threat, call 9-1-1.

DON'T FORGET!
Chapter 4 Summary

- **Rampaging Pachyderms** are employees with a psychiatric disorder (diagnosed or undiagnosed) who experience a significantly disruptive episode of poor behavior at work.
- **How do you identify Rampaging Pachyderms?**
  - Their behavior feels like it's straight out of a movie and you almost can't believe you're seeing what you're seeing.
- **How do you manage/supervise Rampaging Pachyderms? (During an outburst)**
  - Maintain a calm and quiet demeanor.
  - Take note of your surroundings.
  - Determine if the "charge" is real or an empty threat.
  - Call for back up. (If the situation warrants, call 9-1-1 for police assistance.)
  - Follow your plan for intervention.
  - Document, document, document.

5
I RECOGNIZE THE ELEPHANTS IN MY OFFICE, NOW WHAT?

To quote the end of every 1980's *G.I. Joe* television episode, "Knowing is half the battle."

By acknowledging the fact that there are employees in your office experiencing episodes of poor mental health and knowing how to spot them, you are already lightyears ahead of managers from previous generations. Congrats! Nice job! But don't kick back and relax just yet, your work has really just begun.

It's now time for action. Specifically, creation of an action plan tailored to the management of your current and future elephants. The plan includes three steps:

- Observe
- Question
- Intervene

OBSERVE

Use your knowledge and the resources available to you (this book, your HR Department, consultants, etc.) to gauge employee behavior over time. Everyone experiences a bad day or a tough week. That's not the same as consistent patterns of behavior that emerge over several days or months. As the boss, make it a priority to engage your employees frequently enough that you can spot concerning behavior early and not be blindsided by a Rampaging Pachyderm!

Use this helpful checklist from an employee assistance program to identify specific behaviors that might signal an employee in distress.[14]

Absenteeism

- Excessive sick leave with increasingly unbelievable reasons
- Repeated absences, particularly if they follow a pattern
- Tardiness – at the beginning of the work shift or after breaks
- Leaving work early

On-The-Job Absenteeism

- At work but not at their desk or assigned location
- Constantly on their personal phone or tablet
- Long coffee breaks, lunch breaks
- Frequent trips to the restroom or breakroom
- Sleeping on the job

Uneven Work Pattern

- Alternate periods of high and low productivity

Difficulty Concentrating

- Work requires greater effort
- Jobs take more time
- Repeated mistakes due to inattention
- Missed deadlines
- Making bad decisions or using poor judgment
- Errors in written communication
- Forgetfulness

Confusion/Memory Problems

- Difficulty following instructions
- Increasing difficulty handling complex assignments
- Difficulty in recalling instructions, details, conversations, etc.

Poor Employee Relationships on the Job

- Failure to keep promises and unreasonable excuses for failing to keep promises
- Over-reaction to real or imagined criticism
- Borrowing money from coworkers
- Unreasonable resentments
- Avoidance of associates
- Lying and exaggerating
- Complaints from coworkers, supervisors, other staff
- Blames others for problems

Appearance

- Decreasing attention to personal appearance and hygiene
- Odor of alcohol on breath
- Glassy, red eyes
- Tremors
- Inability to walk steadily
- Slurred speech

Other Behaviors

- Withdraws from others, isolates self
- Mood swings
- Increasing irritability
- Relates problems at home, with relationships, with finances, etc.
- Abrupt, radical changes in behavior, (i.e. violent outbursts)

If you believe an employee represents a danger to themselves or others based on their behavior, get them to a safe location, stay with them (if appropriate), and notify Human Resources immediately.

QUESTION

Once you observe behaviors significant enough to cause concern, move to the next step, Question. This is actually the toughest part of the plan. It involves a delicate balance between caring about your employee, wanting to help, and not breaking the law. Federal guidelines related to employment prohibit a manager from asking questions related to the following:

Age, gender, marital status, religious beliefs, political ideology, pregnancy status or information related to children, height, weight, prescribed medications, tobacco use, alcohol use, race, cultural background, physical or mental health conditions (including any disabilities), and medical history.

With so many restrictions, even well-intentioned supervisors can easily cross the line into potentially litigious territory. Before you talk to an employee about subjects that may even approach this line, you should contact your HR partner for tips and recommendations. It's important that you have prepared appropriately so you can have a conversation that meets both the personal and professional needs of the employee, and stay safely in the legal zone as a representative of the employer.

Here are some examples to illustrate what you can and can't say to an employee.

Examples of what **not** to say:

- You are so moody this week. Are you pregnant again or do you need to get on some medication?
- You seem to be sick all the time. Maybe you need to drop the natural methods and see a real doctor.
- Is your spouse cheating on you or something? You are so sensitive lately.

Examples of what to say instead:

- I have noticed a shift in your behavior. Here is the contact information for our Employee Assistance Program. You can use this to arrange free counseling. Is there anything work-related I can help you address?

- You have missed quite a bit of work lately and there are important projects being dropped or not done at all. Part of your employee benefits package includes sick time in addition to medical and pharmacy coverage. Here's the benefits contact person in HR if you need more details. Is there something I can do to help you get organized/back on track?
- I noticed in our meeting today that you were very defensive about your project. That's out of character for you. Is something preventing you from doing your best work?

INTERVENE

It's very likely that some of your Amazing Mammoths and Invisible Elephants will slip past the Question phase and not show up on anyone's radar until something draws attention to them. Regardless of how it happens, when an employee's poor performance and/or behavior negatively affects coworkers, the business, customers, clients, or financial success, it's time to intervene.

Intervention will look different at each company because jobs, rules, and safety measures vary by industry. As a manager or supervisor, you are expected to learn your company's specific policies and procedures related to employee performance and understand when and how to

My personal guiding principle when deciding whether or not to go through the PIP process is the 60% rule. The manager, through conversations and talking it out with HR, should feel at least 60% confident that the performance issue will be successfully resolved and the person will be able to perform their job without further micromanagement after the PIP. If a manager is less than 60% confident that the employee will be successful, a PIP should not be used and instead there should be a discussion of other ways to coach the employee up or out.

–Andrea Sides Herron

Know the rules for your organization and follow them. When in doubt, ask your Human Resources experts for guidance. This is not the time to make it up as you go.

implement those policies and procedures. We can't emphasize this enough.

Performance Improvement Plan

The Human Resources industry standard for addressing the poor performance of an employee is creation and execution of a Performance Improvement Plan (PIP).

Performance Improvement Plans look different for each person and each business; however, they share a few basic elements:

- Specific task/job duty that must be improved
- Examples of specific instances when the employee did not perform as expected
- SMART goals that are achievable, relevant and time-bound
- The length of time reasonably needed to improve the job duty and reach set goals (PIPs usually last 30, 60, or 90 days)
- Resources available to help the employee succeed
- Scheduled times to review progress and discuss next steps
- List of consequences if PIP isn't successfully completed

A few important notes about the PIP:

- A PIP should be used when there is a commitment to help the employee improve, not as a way for a frustrated manager to start the termination process.
- Conversations about performance concerns should take place with the employee before they are given a PIP. It should never be a surprise.
- If the manager and HR partner decide to assign a PIP, tell the employee in advance of the scheduled meeting so they have time to prepare.
- HR should review the plan with a focus on removing any bias against the employee.
- The manager should ensure all progress meetings are scheduled and occur on time.

A second kind of intervention that is similar to the PIP is a management tactic called "coaching them out." In an article for The Balance Careers, Dan McCarthy defined this concept as follows:

"Coaching someone out of a job is helping the employee to understand that it's in his/her best interest to leave voluntarily. It's giving them the option of finding another role, internally or externally, that's a better fit for their skills, giving them the opportunity to be more successful."[15]

We advise the use of extreme caution with this approach. Don't venture down the path of coaching someone out without assistance from your HR professionals. They will instruct you to document everything that happens and be very clear and factual about specific work performance issues. Documentation is critical when addressing the poor performance of an employee experiencing a period of adjustment or an episode of poor mental health and may help decrease the risk of an employee feeling retaliated against—especially if this process occurs after they disclose a mental illness or psychiatric disability.

Did we say document everything?

Document, document, document.

Write it down or it didn't happen.

Seriously.

We also recommend that before you try to make an employee "understand that it's in his/her best interest to leave voluntarily", remember that these elephants are struggling because of an external stressor or miscommunicating neurotransmitters. It's not a case of being lazy or defiant. Additionally, uneven work patterns, confusion, memory problems, and difficulty concentrating can't be "cured" by pointing out every reason the employee can't or won't be successful in their current role.

Moving someone to a new department won't change the fact that they live with a mental illness; however, having an engaged manager with both knowledge and a plan could mean the difference between an unfortunate termination and a resilient comeback.

Put on some "perspectacles"

ASHLEY SIDES JOHNSON

Unless you have personal experience with a mental health condition, you can't really understand what your employee is feeling. To give you some perspective on what an episode of poor mental health feels like for the employee experiencing it, I'm going to share a bit of my personal story.

The path to mental health crisis is long, twisted, and filled with unexpected detours. For years, my mood disorder remained well controlled. I could handle deadlines and huge piles of work with no problem. Then, I had to change medication. Coming off a medicine I'd taken for years was bad enough. My brain protested loudly about the shift in chemical levels. I felt confused, tired, and inexplicably annoyed. Because it takes about 4 weeks for a new psychiatric medication to fully take effect, you don't know if something will work or not for a long time. That makes the process of finding the right medication and the right dose a seemingly never-ending quest.

As the months of trying new meds (and having terrible side effects with each one) passed, I felt exhausted and overwhelmed. The simplest task seemed so hard. Normal bumps in the road became insurmountable obstacles. I couldn't concentrate. I couldn't focus.

My brain didn't seem to work anymore. Usually, it was sharp and witty and ready to handle anything, but now it was a jumble of noise and never-ending thoughts. It was so loud in my head. How did no one else hear it?

I had to pump myself up to leave the office and do my job. I fake smiled and fake mingled and fake paid attention. I pulled off events and coordinated major activities then collapsed into my chair once they were over.

Communicating required so much effort. So, after a while, I just didn't. I didn't answer the phone or return phone calls in a timely manner. I didn't tell my boss the status of projects. I didn't go to meetings. I slowly disconnected from work, but I was still physically there.

By this point, I realized how bad things were and that the best course for my personal well-being was to take FMLA or a leave of absence and really work on feeling better. But...

There was so much work to do

My team needed me

No one else had my skill set and could easily step in

I didn't know how to ask for a "leave"

I didn't want to tell anyone how sick I was

I didn't want people whispering about me and why I wasn't at work

I just didn't want to talk about it

Eventually, my managers got involved due to my performance levels—and they were right to do so—however, what followed was a frustrating, embarrassing, and lengthy process I don't wish on anyone.

So, on behalf of the people in your office who have a mental illness or disorder, please do not do these things when and if they are struggling:

What not to do as the boss:

- Make their job so miserable that they quit or want to quit

- Take away the parts of their job they love the most

- Prevent them from engaging with others, i.e. isolate them

- Punish them with completely unexpected bad reviews

- Tell them you will do something helpful and then do the opposite

- Embarrass them in front of coworkers and teammates

To sum up, creating a strong, solid, and compassionate action plan tailored to the management of your current and future elephants will set you apart as a leader. Your plan may serve as the early intervention an employee needs to avert self-harm and recover. Your thoughtful questions could generate a true moment of clarity for someone trying to find their way. This is your chance as a manager to increase the odds of a positive outcome for everyone involved. And, yes, anytime you work with people, you assume risk. That's why we encourage you to plan ahead and work with your legal and HR experts to minimize organizational risk and avoid triggering a stampede.

A word of caution: Sometimes, your best efforts to observe, question, and intervene won't be enough. People have free will to make their own choices and there's nothing you can do to change that.

True Story: Danny

Danny worked nearly 20 years as an I.T. technician in a large company. About three years before he left the organization, a close relative was the victim of a homicide. The incident rocked his world and he was never the same. For a while, Danny's boss tried to be understanding about the angry outbursts at coworkers and visible hostility when working with others. Surely the unfathomable tragedy experienced by the employee and his family caused this irritability and moodiness. But how long do you allow poor behavior to continue with no consequences?

One afternoon, the boss asked Danny to stop by the office. In a confidential setting, the boss told Danny that his behavior had changed. "This isn't you, Danny. What's going on? Talk to me," said the boss. Danny declined to talk to the boss about his personal feelings or behavior. (Which is his right as an employee.)

As time moved on, Danny's behavior did not change and the boss followed the disciplinary process related to incidents of unacceptable behavior. Eventually, Danny chose to leave the organization but did so with many strained relationships in his wake.

More than a year later, local police received word that Danny was missing. They searched several areas in the city and ultimately located Danny's vehicle on the company's property. Because it was after hours on a weekend, law enforcement needed help accessing the building.

The security person on duty escorted officers inside the facility and opened doors as needed. They eventually found Danny in a remote part of the office. He was deceased, having died by suicide.

As news of this discovery spread, Danny's former managers and coworkers were distraught. They knew something in him changed after the death of his relative. They gave him space. They intervened. They tried to help. But you can't force people into treatment if they haven't broken the law or threatened to harm themselves or others.

The moral of this story is the company used their available tools to try and help Danny. As an employer, they did everything they could without infringing on his right to privacy, but despite their best efforts, the situation still ended in tragedy. Sadly, sometimes it happens this way.

DON'T FORGET!
Chapter 5 Summary

- **Create a 3-step action plan:**
  - Observe
  - Question
  - Intervene
- **Know the rules** for your organization and follow them. Do not make it up as you go.
- **A performance improvement plan (PIP)** is a tool for addressing the poor performance of an employee.
  - Use a PIP to help the employee improve, not as a way to start the termination process.
  - If a manager is less than 60% confident that the employee will be successful, don't use a PIP.
- **Don't try "coaching someone out"** without assistance from your HR professionals.
- **Sometimes, your best efforts won't be enough.** People have free will to make their own choices. Their behavior is not your fault.

6
RULES AND REGULATIONS

The next two chapters are important but much more technical. As you read, just keep in mind that you need this knowledge to successfully manage the elephants in your office…and avoid going to jail for discrimination.

While there are thousands of state and federal guidelines related to employment, arguably the most important document to know when managing employees with a mental health condition is the Americans with Disabilities Act (ADA).

Title I of the Americans with Disabilities Act of 1990 prohibits private employers, state and local governments, employment agencies and labor unions from discriminating against qualified individuals with disabilities in job application procedures, hiring, firing, advancement, compensation, job training, and other terms, conditions, and privileges of employment. (Applicable for employers with 15 or more employees.)

In the document, an individual with a disability is defined as a person who:

- Has a physical or mental impairment that substantially limits one or more major life activities;
- Has a record of such an impairment; or
- Is regarded as having such an impairment.

Apparently, inclusion of the phrase "mental impairment" generated a lot of concern and discussion across the country. Employers, patients, advocates, and lawyers wanted answers to a bevy of questions related to the proper interpretation of "mental" and "impairment." To their credit, the EEOC stepped in and offered some guidance.

"After receiving large numbers of claims alleging employment discrimination based on psychiatric disability, the U.S. Equal Employment Opportunity Commission (EEOC) created an enforcement guide to 'set forth the Commission's position on the application of Title I of the Americans with Disabilities Act of 1990 to individuals with psychiatric disabilities.'"[16]

Short version—The ADA applies to employees with a psychiatric disability.

Only a handful of you need or want to read the entire EEOC enforcement guide, so the key points from the document—related to managing elephants—appear below in a Q&A format.

Americans with Disabilities Act (ADA) and Psychiatric Disability—What You Need to Know

Q. What constitutes a psychiatric disability under the ADA?
A. Someone who:
- Has a physical or mental impairment that substantially limits one or more major life activities;
- Has a record of such an impairment; or
- Is regarded as having such an impairment.

Q. What is a "mental impairment" under the ADA?
A. Any mental or psychological disorder. Examples include major depression, bipolar disorder, anxiety disorders (which include panic disorder, obsessive-compulsive disorder, and posttraumatic stress disorder), schizophrenia, and personality disorders.

Q. Is every diagnosis in the DSM-V considered a disability?
A. Not all conditions listed in the Diagnostic and Statistical Manual of Mental Disorders, Fifth Edition (DSM-V) are disabilities, or even impairments, for purposes of the ADA. Even if a condition is an impairment, it is not automatically a "disability." To rise to the level of a "disability," an impairment must "substantially limit" one or more major life activities of the individual.

Q. Should the corrective effects of medications be considered when deciding if an impairment is so severe that it substantially limits a major life activity?
A. No. An individual who is taking medication for a mental impairment has an ADA disability if there is evidence that the mental impairment, when left untreated, substantially limits a major life activity.

Q. Can an employer ask job applicants (on a job application) if they have a psychiatric disability?
A. No. An employer may not ask questions that are likely to elicit information about a disability before making an offer of employment.

Q. Are employees with a psychiatric disability required to disclose that to the employer?
A. No.

Q. As an employer, do I have to provide an employee with reasonable accommodations?
A. Yes. Read Chapter 7 for details.

Q. Can you fire someone with a psychiatric disability?
A. Yes. The Americans with Disabilities Act was created to protect disabled people from employment discrimination. It does not give them a free pass to act however they please with no consequences. According to the ADA and supported by the EEOC, employers can fire workers with disabilities under three conditions[17]:

- The termination is unrelated to the disability or
- The employee does not meet legitimate requirements for the job, such as performance or production standards, with or without a reasonable accommodation or
- Because of the employee's disability, he or she poses a direct threat to health or safety in the workplace.

Example: An employee physically assaults the department director in the workplace, during work hours. The company has a policy that says any employee who behaves violently toward a supervisor or coworker is immediately terminated.

Can you terminate an employee with a known mental illness for this behavior? Yes. That employee broke a conduct and safety policy unilaterally applied to each and every employee regardless of position, seniority, or disability status.

Q. What is the "direct threat" standard under the ADA?
A. Direct threat means a significant risk of substantial harm to the employee or others that cannot be reduced or eliminated by reasonable accommodations. An employer may lawfully exclude a person from employment (not hire them) only if the employer can show the person represents a direct threat.

Q. Does an employee with a psychiatric disability automatically pose a "direct threat"?
A. No. The employer must identify specific behavior that could pose a direct threat. The existence of a psychiatric disability isn't enough. To maintain compliance, employers must apply the direct threat standard uniformly and may not use safety concerns to justify excluding people with disabilities.

Q. What is a charge of discrimination?
A. A charge of discrimination is a signed statement asserting that an employer, union or labor organization engaged in employment discrimination. It requests the EEOC to take remedial action.[18]

Q. Is there a time limit on filing a charge of discrimination?
A. Employees or applicants have 180 calendar days from the day the discrimination took place to file a charge of discrimination. The 180-calendar-day filing deadline is extended to 300 calendar days if a state or local agency enforces a law that prohibits employment discrimination on the same basis.[19]

Chapter 6 Summary

- **The ADA applies to employees with a psychiatric disability.**
- Psychiatric disability means someone who:
    - Has a physical or mental impairment that substantially limits one or more major life activities;
    - Has a record of such an impairment; or
    - Is regarded as having such an impairment.
- Not all impairments are disabilities.
- Employees with a psychiatric disability are not required to disclose that information to an employer.
- Employees can file a charge of discrimination against a company, employer, or labor organization.
- A charge of discrimination must be filed with the EEOC within 180 days of the alleged act.

7
REASONABLE ACCOMMODATIONS

This chapter could have been titled "ADA and Reasonable Accommodations: An Employer's Worst Nightmare" or "Reasonable Accommodations (and the reasons we hate them)" or "Reasonable Accommodations are an Undue Hardship on My Bottom Line."

Why all the hate for such a seemingly innocent concept? Decades upon decades ago, our business forefathers decided that reasonable accommodations were really just special treatment for people who couldn't do a job. The archaic notion took root and out of it grew a culture of silence where people with psychiatric disabilities pretend they don't need workplace accommodations. Dare we say they attempt to be invisible in the office...

So, we're putting forth a radical idea—reasonable accommodations are good for business.

Will the customer experience truly be compromised if Sally Employee works in a quiet space or has permission to attend her monthly therapy appointment?

Will profits tank because Jonny Employee uses a personalized "to-do" list to keep him on track?

No. We believe employees allowed, even encouraged, to meet their basic emotional needs will be more productive, incur fewer absences, and feel greater loyalty to the company.

Healthier employee = Healthier business

What follows is a summary of what you need to know about reasonable accommodations and discrimination. As in Chapter 6, some of the information is highly procedural but really important if you want to successfully manage the elephants in your office.

Reasonable accommodations and discrimination

The fundamental purpose of the Americans with Disabilities Act (ADA) is "to provide a clear and comprehensive national mandate for the elimination of discrimination against individuals with disabilities." The stated "proper goals" regarding individuals with disabilities are to "assure equality of opportunity, full participation, independent living, and economic self-sufficiency for such individuals."

Translation for our purposes – People experiencing an episode of poor mental health deserve the same opportunity to work and make money as everyone else.

That being said, employees experiencing short-term or long-term mental health conditions might be more successful with modifications to their work environment. Enter—reasonable accommodations.

"A reasonable accommodation is a modification or adjustment to a job, the work environment, or the way things usually are done that enables a qualified individual with a disability to enjoy an equal employment opportunity."[20]

An employee in a wheelchair needs access to an elevator.

A deaf employee needs an interpreter during large meetings.

These are common examples of reasonable accommodations related to employees with physical disabilities. But what about employees with a qualified psychiatric disability?

Examples of reasonable accommodations for employees with psychiatric disabilities

Change scheduled work hours – to include part-time employment, use of accrued paid leave for treatment or recovery periods, and a consistent schedule

Alter the environment to increase concentration – to include room dividers/partitions, use of headphones or white noise machine, and moving employee away from busy conference rooms

Restructure work tasks – to include use of organizational tools, dividing large tasks into smaller steps, providing instructions in writing, and scheduling weekly meetings with a supervisor or mentor to keep employee on track

Modify break schedules – to include leaving work area as needed to address symptoms, flexibility in the timing of lunch break (not duration), and permission to schedule condition-related appointments during the work day (using accrued time off if necessary)

Reasonable accommodations in the workplace can also look like this.

True Story: Shonte

An interesting note, and an example of the larger picture, is the fact that I've had very few requests in my HR career for ADA accommodations. Employers don't want to educate on it for fear that they'll promote creating accommodations and have people abuse it for less time at work and lower productivity. Employees either don't know they can request accommodations or they don't want to because they are afraid of retaliation or stigma related to specific conditions.

–Andrea Sides Herron

Shonte had been physically assaulted by a male prior to getting her current job. She had PTSD from the assault and was triggered by being in small spaces alone with men. Shonte's role was a customer service agent and part of this job did include occasionally being one of the last people on the floor with customers in small areas. As an accommodation, Shonte did not typically work the closing shift. If there were no other options and she was needed to close, Shonte was given other duties to close down instead of staying with customers until the end. The customer service team also created a new safety measure that allowed anyone who was in an uncomfortable situation to quickly and discreetly call for backup using a seemingly innocuous code phrase.

True Story: Lexi

Lexi has a diagnosis of bipolar disorder and works in a school cafeteria. Her primary responsibilities include washing dishes, stocking the shelves, and replenishing food on the serving line. Her manager said for the new school year Lexi's duties would also include working the cash register. The thought of being responsible for money, the fear of counting incorrectly, and the pressure of the fast-paced environment caused her serious distress. Lexi requested a reasonable accommodation from her employer—to not work the cash register. This was a reasonable request because she continued to do the job she was hired to do and having another employee handle the cash register did not put undue hardship on the school.

To be compliant with the rules of the ADA, employers must provide **reasonable** accommodation to qualified individuals with disabilities who are applicants or employees unless doing so causes undue **hardship**. Key words—reasonable, hardship.

To figure out if an employee's request for accommodation will cause undue hardship, answer these questions:

1. Is the employee's request reasonable given the overall resources of the business/organization?
2. What is the net cost to the employer to meet the request?
3. Will the request disrupt the nature or operation of the business?

Not every request can be granted in the exact way it's presented; however, employers are encouraged to work with the employee to find an acceptable solution. If the original accommodation is cost-prohibitive or disrupts the nature of the business, brainstorm alternative options. The whole point of accommodation is to find a new way to overcome a disability so all employees can successfully contribute to their organization.

In some cases, the request will not be reasonable or attainable. Employers can legally deny a request for reasonable accommodation after conducting an individualized assessment of the employee, current company data, and overall impact on the business. To be compliant with the ADA, the assessment should clearly show specific reasons why the requested accommodation would cause significant difficulty or expense for the employer.

If you think a request for accommodation should be denied, we highly recommend checking with your HR and legal teams before taking any action. This part of the process is exactly where discrimination lawsuits are born.

Examples of **Unreasonable** Accommodation Requests:

Request: An employee with depression requests a skylight be created over their cubicle because natural light helps their mood.
Denial: The company is a small accounting firm that rents space in a larger office building. As part of their lease agreement, they cannot alter the physical integrity of the building. The employer can deny the request because renegotiating a lease agreement to include provisions for one employee causes significant difficulty. As an alternative solution, the company could approve a light therapy lamp for the employee's cubicle. With this arrangement, the employee receives the necessary accommodation and the business doesn't experience undue hardship.

Request: An employee's regular work schedule is 10 AM to 4 PM. The employee requests full-time pay as a reasonable accommodation because they can't get out of bed and get to work any earlier.
Denial: The purpose of the ADA is to prevent unfair treatment based on a qualified disability. This request seeks to alter salary and wage policies to accommodate an employee who already works part-time hours. It does not create equal opportunity in the workplace.

Request: An employee experiences fatigue in the middle of the day and needs to rest. The employee asks for an accommodation to allow him to take a nap on the couch in the middle of the office every day around lunch time.
Denial: Sleeping in the middle of the office during the work day disrupts the operation of the business and is, therefore, not reasonable. **However**, employers are encouraged to seek an acceptable, alternative solution to relatively unreasonable requests. In this case, you could brainstorm with the employee to identify other locations in the office for a nap that would be less distracting to others. (This back and forth dialogue is called the "interactive process." Read more about it in a few paragraphs.)

Request: An employee experiencing an episode of poor mental health wants to send an email to their team detailing physical and mental symptoms they are facing. She says this will help others better understand her behavior.

Denial: Employees have a right to not know personal information about their coworkers and/or managers. Oversharing protected health information can transfer the burden of the employee's illness to the staff.

HOW THE PROCESS WORKS INSIDE THE ORGANIZATION

The Human Resources Department guides the process of addressing an employee's request for reasonable accommodation. Industry best practice prescribes how to create, implement, and/or review organizational policies and procedures for handling requests for disability accommodations, including requests for psychiatric-related disability.

Rules for requesting reasonable accommodation

- An employee **must** make a request for reasonable accommodation.
- The request does **not** have to be in writing.
- The request does **not** have to specifically mention the ADA or the term "reasonable accommodation."
- The request **must** ask for a change at work (time off, modified break periods, consistent work hours, etc.) for a reason related to a medical condition.
- "Plain English" used to describe a medical condition is acceptable i.e. "completely stressed out" instead of "experiencing a recurrence of Generalized Anxiety Disorder."
- An employee may request reasonable accommodations at any time during employment.
- A job applicant may request reasonable accommodations at any time during the hiring process.

Once a request for reasonable accommodation has been made to the manager or Human Resources representative, the process of assessment begins.

In many instances, the need for accommodation and the most appropriate solution are obvious. This tends to happen more with recognizable physical disabilities. When the medical condition and need for accommodation are not obvious (like most psychiatric disabilities), the EEOC recommends evaluating the request through a flexible, interactive process.

The interactive process includes the employee, employer, and health care providers as necessary. The goal is to identify the precise job-related limitations experienced by the employee and discuss accommodations to overcome those limitations. Essentially, the employer should make a "good faith" effort to engage the employee in problem solving.

The Office of Disability Employment Policy, a service of the U.S. Department of Labor, wants to help employers and employees find accommodations that lead to success. To that end, they developed the Job Accommodation Network (JAN) as the "leading source of free, expert and confidential guidance on workplace accommodations and disability employment issues."

The website, www.askjan.org, has a plethora of information related to disability and employment in general but also a robust section dedicated to mental health impairments. If you would like more examples or additional resources about a particular scenario, go here: https://askjan.org/disabilities/Mental-Health-Impairments.cfm

Chapter 7 Summary

- A reasonable accommodation is a modification or adjustment to a job, the work environment, or the way things usually are done that enables a qualified individual with a disability to enjoy an equal employment opportunity.
- Reasonable accommodations for employees with psychiatric disabilities could include:
  - Changing scheduled work hours
  - Altering the environment to increase concentration
  - Restructuring work tasks
  - Modifying break schedules
- Employers must provide reasonable accommodation to qualified individuals with disabilities who are applicants or employees unless doing so causes undue hardship.
- Employers are encouraged to work with the employee to find an acceptable solution.
- **Reasonable accommodations are good for business.**

ONE HUNDRED FIRST CONGRESS OF THE UNITED STATES OF AMERICA

AT THE SECOND SESSION

Begun and held at the City of Washington on Tuesday, the twenty-third day of January, one thousand nine hundred and ninety

An Act to establish a clear and comprehensive prohibition of discrimination on the basis of disability.

Americans with Disabilities Act of 1990, AS AMENDED with ADA Amendments Act of 2008[22]

TITLE 42 - THE PUBLIC HEALTH AND WELFARE
CHAPTER 126 - EQUAL OPPORTUNITY FOR INDIVIDUALS WITH DISABILITIES

A. SUBCHAPTER I - EMPLOYMENT

Sec. 12111. Definitions

(9) Reasonable accommodation

The term "reasonable accommodation" may include

(A) making existing facilities used by employees readily accessible to and usable by individuals with disabilities; and

(B) job restructuring, part-time or modified work schedules, reassignment to a vacant position, acquisition or modification of equipment or devices, appropriate adjustment or modifications of examinations, training materials or policies, the provision of qualified readers or interpreters, and other similar accommodations for individuals with disabilities.

A. SUBCHAPTER I - EMPLOYMENT

Sec. 12111. Definitions

(10) Undue hardship

(A) In general

The term "undue hardship" means an action requiring significant difficulty or expense, when considered in light of the factors set forth in subparagraph (B).

(B) Factors to be considered

In determining whether an accommodation would impose an undue hardship on a covered entity, factors to be considered include

(i) the nature and cost of the accommodation needed under this chapter;

(ii) the overall financial resources of the facility or facilities involved in the provision of the reasonable accommodation; the number of persons employed at such facility; the effect on expenses and resources, or the impact otherwise of such accommodation upon the operation of the facility;

(iii) the overall financial resources of the covered entity; the overall size of the business of a covered entity with respect to the number of its employees; the number, type, and location of its facilities; and

(iv) the type of operation or operations of the covered entity, including the composition, structure, and functions of the workforce of such entity; the geographic separateness, administrative, or fiscal relationship of the facility or facilities in question to the covered entity.

Sec. 12112. Discrimination

(5)

(A) not making reasonable accommodations to the known physical or mental limitations of an otherwise qualified individual with a disability who is an applicant or employee, unless such covered entity can demonstrate that the accommodation would impose an undue hardship on the operation of the business of such covered entity; or

(B) denying employment opportunities to a job applicant or employee who is an otherwise qualified individual with a disability, if such denial is based on the need of such covered entity to make reasonable accommodation to the physical or mental impairments of the employee or applicant;

8
FIGHT STIGMA WITH EDUCATION

If you want all employees to meet performance goals and positively contribute to the financial bottom line, talk about mental and emotional health.

If you want to rid the office of stigma related to psychiatric disorders, educate your staff.

How?

Set a date. Your company probably allows adjustments to benefit plans once a year during open enrollment. Make the most of this opportunity by scheduling education related to mental health and well-being during the open enrollment period. If that time doesn't work well for your department, try May—it's national Mental Health Awareness Month. If that doesn't work, pick a date—any date—just make it a priority to meet.

Be clear and transparent. Tell employees about their rights in the workplace, what services are available, how to access those services, and who is allowed to know what regarding these services.

Topics covered in your department education could include:

- Common external stressors that could lead to "adjustment disorders"
- The most common mental health disorders found in the workplace

A FEW WORDS ABOUT THE EAP

In most organizations, an Employee Assistance Program (EAP) is a benefit of employment like life insurance or short-term disability coverage. You get the benefit because you work there. It is not connected to medical insurance or a particular health plan.

EAP is also the most underutilized employee benefit.

A lot of people tell me they won't use the EAP because they don't want anyone to "know their business." Let me assure you that no one knows what happens in the EAP. Personal issues discussed with your provider are heavily protected through privacy laws. Human Resources does not get a list of names, locations, demographics, etc. of the employees who use the services. We literally get an invoice stating our monthly utilization so we can pay the providers accurately. Nothing more.

One of the best things you can do as a manager is encourage use of the EAP. It is a free benefit. No strings attached. Your employee and their household can use the services to address events or situations negatively impacting their well-being. Employers provide this benefit because it BENEFITS everyone!

–Andrea Sides Herron

- Company-specific resources to help employees manage pre-existing, developing, or worsening episodes of poor mental health. This is usually called an EAP, Employee Assistance Program, and provides access to counselors, therapists, addiction treatment resources, and much more.
- Contact information for suicide prevention hotlines, local behavioral health resources, and where to go if someone experiences a mental health emergency
- The ADA, Americans with Disabilities Act, and how it applies to both physical and psychiatric disabilities
- The definition of reasonable accommodations and examples of what that looks like in your specific work environment
- The internal process for requesting FMLA (Family Medical Leave Act) or leaves of absence
- **What coworkers and supervisors *CAN* do to help someone in distress**

Normalizing conversations about mental health enables employees to identify their needs and take corrective action sooner. It also creates a more supportive environment for the elephants in your office allowing them to concentrate on work and not staving off a panic attack. True, it may increase the utilization of certain employee benefits, but as mentioned throughout this book, an emotionally safe workspace boosts productivity, attendance rates, financial performance, recruitment, and retention efforts. Healthier employee = Healthier business.

When discussing suicide, words matter

In the unfortunate circumstance you must discuss an employee's death with your team/department, consider these suggestions from *The Recommendations for Reporting on Suicide*[21]:

Inform but spare the details.

- Don't describe the method of death (shot himself, hung himself with a rope, overdosed on a bunch of sleeping pills, etc.).
- If the person left a note, do not detail what the note contained or call it a "suicide note."

As a supervisor, you have no real knowledge of what your employees have experienced in their lifetime. They may have lost a parent or close friend to suicide. They might have considered ending their own life. They could be struggling with thoughts of suicide every day. To avoid inadvertently triggering an episode of PTSD or poor mental health in your employees, please think about what you say before you say it. Your off-the-cuff remark might rip open an old wound you don't even know exists.

Also, as a personal request, try to never use the phrase, "that's so selfish" when discussing a person who died by suicide. It doesn't matter if the deceased is a celebrity, employee, or even a person in the news. That person experienced something so terrible, so painful, so suffocating, that dying seemed the only way out. Unless you have walked a mile in those shoes and fought with a brain that abandoned logic, you have no idea what they were thinking.

–Ashley Sides Johnson

Choose your words carefully.

- **Do not use the term "committed suicide."** Instead use "died by suicide," "completed suicide," "killed him/herself," or "ended his/her life."
- Do not refer to suicide as "successful," "unsuccessful" or a "failed attempt."
- Do not describe a suicide as "inexplicable" or "without warning."

National Suicide Prevention Lifeline
Talk: 1-800-273-TALK (8255)
Chat: www.suicidepreventionlifeline.org

DON'T FORGET!
Chapter 8 Summary

- Educate your staff about mental and emotional health topics
  - Set a date to meet
  - Be clear and transparent about available services
- Encourage use of the Employee Assistance Program (EAP)
- When discussing suicide, words matter
  - Inform but spare the details
  - Do not say "committed suicide"
  - Try saying "died by suicide"
- National Suicide Prevention Lifeline 1-800-273-TALK (8255)

CONCLUSION

In this book, we have given you the tools and information needed to successfully identify and support the elephants in your office. With approximately 1 in 5 adults in the U.S.—43.8 million, or 18.5%—experiencing mental illness in a given year, someone in your workplace is struggling.

By implementing a few strategies and sharing this knowledge with your staff, you not only become a strong, memorable, and respected leader, but you can create an environment that enables everyone to do the job they were hired to do.

We believe employees allowed, even encouraged, to meet their basic emotional needs will be more productive, incur fewer absences, and feel greater loyalty to the company. That behavior goes a long way toward meeting performance, business, and financial expectations.

Bottom line – you can meet people where they are, show empathy, and find new ways to accomplish tasks without jeopardizing your career, office morale, or the business.

 =

ABOUT THE AUTHORS

ANDREA SIDES HERRON, MA, PHR, SHRM-CP

Andrea has worked in a variety of human resources positions across diverse business sectors. Her experience includes service to the Oregon Humane Society, Berry Global, and WebMD among others. She earned multiple certifications in Human Resources Management and Coaching from national accrediting bodies including Social + Emotional Intelligence Certified Coach through ISEI, Fierce Conversation methodology, and Personalysis Coach and Facilitator.

With advanced training in executive coaching, culture change and alignment, merger and acquisition facilitation, Andrea helps employees and leaders find success in challenging situations. She also advocates passionately for diversity and inclusion in the workforce.

Andrea earned a Bachelor of Arts degree in Psychology and a Master of Arts degree in Industrial/Organizational Psychology from Western Kentucky University. She lives in Portland, Oregon with her family.

ASHLEY SIDES JOHNSON, MA

A communication specialist in the marketing and public relations field, Ashley has spent the past 13 years working in health care. Areas of focus include the Community Health Needs Assessment, Hospital Incident Command System, and content creation. She served on the Society for Healthcare Strategy and Market Development (SHSMD) Editorial Advisory Board to provide content advising and as a faculty member for the SHSMD U educational series.

Ashley is an advocate for homeless services and played an instrumental role in creating the Homeless Medical Respite Program at United Caring Services in Evansville, IN. She writes about parenting and mental health on her blog, ASJ Explains, and serves as a contributing author for *The Mighty* and *Scary Mommy*.

Ashley earned a Bachelor of Arts degree in Government from Centre College in Danville, KY, and a Master of Arts degree in Communication from Western Kentucky University. She lives in Henderson, Kentucky with her family.

RESOURCES

WORKPLACE MENTAL HEALTH

Job Accommodation Network
A service of the U.S. Department of Labor's Office of Disability
Employment Policy
www.askjan.org

Center for Workplace Mental Health
A service of the American Psychiatric Association Foundation
www.workplacementalhealth.org

Mental Health America
Workplace Mental Health
http://www.mentalhealthamerica.net/workplace-mental-health

National Alliance on Mental Illness (NAMI)
www.nami.org
www.nami.org/Find-Support/Living-with-a-Mental-Health-
Condition/Succeeding-at-Work

SUICIDE/CRISIS

The National Suicide Prevention Lifeline
1-800-273-TALK (8255)
via TTY by dialing 800-799-4889
A free, 24/7 confidential service that can provide people in suicidal crisis or emotional distress, or those around them, with support, information, and local resources.

The Veterans Crisis Line and Military Crisis Line
1-800-273-8255 Press 1
The Veterans Crisis Line and Military Crisis Line connect veterans and service members in crisis and their families and friends with qualified, caring U.S. Department of Veterans Affairs responders.

Crisis Text Line
Text HOME to 741741 from anywhere in the USA to message with a trained crisis counselor.
www.crisistextline.org

The Trevor Project
1-866-488-7386
An LGBT crisis intervention and suicide prevention hotline, 24/7
www.thetrevorproject.org

American Foundation for Suicide Prevention
www.afsp.org

Suicide Awareness Voices of Education
www.save.org

ReportingOnSuicide.org
Guidance and best practices for media and online coverage of suicide.
www.reportingonsuicide.org

ENDNOTES

1   National Institute of Mental Health: Mental Illness. Retrieved (2018, August 2) from https://www.nimh.nih.gov/health/statistics/mental-illness.shtml

2   National Registry of Evidence-based Programs and Practices. Behind the Term: Serious Mental Illness. Prepared in 2016 by Development Services Group, Inc., under contract no. HHSS 2832 0120 0037i/HHSS 2834 2002T, ref. no. 283–12–3702. Retrieved 2018, July 26 from https://nrepp.samhsa.gov/Docs/Literatures/Behind_the_Term_Serious%20%20Mental%20Illness.pdf

3   Kennedy Krieger Institute. Patient Care: Developmental Disorders. Retrieved 2018, July 26 from https://www.kennedykrieger.org/patient-care/diagnoses-disorders/developmental-disorders

4   NAMI. Mental Health Conditions. Retrieved 2018, July 26 from https://www.nami.org/Learn-More/Mental-Health-Conditions

5   WebMD. Adjustment Disorder. Retrieved 2018, July 29 from https://www.webmd.com/mental-health/mental-health-adjustment-disorder#1

6   WebMD. Adjustment Disorder. Retrieved 2018, July 29 from https://www.webmd.com/mental-health/mental-health-adjustment-disorder#1

7   Widera, Eric, MD; Chang, Anna, MD; and Chen, Helen L., MD. (2010, November). *Presenteeism: A Public Health Hazard.* Retrieved from https://www.ncbi.nlm.nih.gov/pmc/articles/PMC2947637/ on 2019, February 7.

8   Hemp, Paul. (2004, October). *Presenteeism: At Work—But Out of It.* Harvard Business Review. October 2004 Issue. Retrieved 2019, February 7 from https://hbr.org/2004/10/presenteeism-at-work-but-out-of-it

9   Schaefer, Patricia. *The Hidden Costs of Presenteeism: Causes and Solutions.* Business Know-How. Last updated 2018, January 18 and retrieved 2019, February 7 from https://www.businessknowhow.com/manage/presenteeism.htm

10   US Department of Labor. Employment Characteristics of Families Summary. USDL-18-0589 (2018, April 19). Retrieved 2019, March 24 from https://www.bls.gov/news.release/famee.nr0.htm

11   American Psychiatric Association. Diagnostic and Statistical Manual of Mental Disorders (DSM–5). Retrieved 2018, July 26 from https://www.psychiatry.org/psychiatrists/practice/dsm

12   NAMI. Know the Warning Signs. Retrieved 2018, July 26 from https://www.nami.org/Learn-More/Know-the-Warning-Signs

13   Nelson, Bryan. (2016, February 4). 15 cute animals that could kill you. Mother Nature Network. Retrieved 2019, March 7 from https://www.mnn.com/earth-matters/animals/photos/15-cute-animals-that-could-kill-you/elephant

14   University of Virginia Medical System. Checklist of Unsatisfactory Job Performance. Retrieved 2019, March 7 from https://www.medicalcenter.virginia.edu/feap/supervisor/checklist.html

15   McCarthy, Dan. (updated 2018, November 4). Learn How to Get an Employee to Quit. The Balance Careers. Retrieved 2019, March 7 from https://www.thebalancecareers.com/how-to-coach-an-employee-out-of-a-job-2275942

16   EEOC Enforcement Guidance on the Americans with Disabilities Act and Psychiatric Disabilities. Notice Number 915.002. Purpose Section. Retrieved 2018, July 29 from https://www.eeoc.gov/policy/docs/psych.html

17   US Department of Labor. Employers and the ADA: Myths and Facts. Retrieved 2018, August 2 from https://www.dol.gov/odep/pubs/fact/ada.htm

18   US Equal Employment Opportunity Commission. Filing A Charge of Discrimination. Retrieved 2019, March 7 from https://www.eeoc.gov/employees/charge.cfm

19   US Equal Employment Opportunity Commission. Time Limits for Filing A Charge. Retrieved 2019, March 8 from https://www.eeoc.gov/employees/timeliness.cfm

20   Job Accommodation Network. Employers' Practical Guide to Reasonable Accommodation Under the Americans with Disabilities Act (ADA). Retrieved 2019, March 12 from https://askjan.org/publications/employers/employers-guide.cfm

21   Greenstein, Laura. (2018, June 15). *Why Suicide Reporting Guidelines Matter.* NAMI Blogs. Retrieved 2019, March 15 from https://www.nami.org/Blogs/NAMI-Blog/June-2018/Why-Suicide-Reporting-Guidelines-Matter

22   AMERICANS WITH DISABILITIES ACT OF 1990, AS AMENDED. Retrieved 2019, March 8 from https://www.ada.gov/pubs/adastatute08.htm

23   Schuster, Sarah. (2017, June). *18 Infuriating Examples of Mental Illness-Shaming No One Should Go Through.* The Mighty. Retrieved 2019, March 15 from https://themighty.com/2017/06/mental-illness-shaming-stigma-discrimination/